HAVE BEEN FULFILLED AMONG US,
JUST AS THEY WERE HANDED DOWN TO US BY THOSE WHO FROM THE FIRST WERE EYEWITNESSES AND SERVANTS OF THE WORD.
WITH THIS IN MIND,
SINCE I MYSELF HAVE CAREFULLY INVESTIGATED EVERYTHING FROM THE BEGINNING,
I TOO DECIDED TO WRITE AN ORDERLY ACCOUNT FOR YOU...

SO THAT YOU MAY KNOW THE CERTAINTY OF THE THINGS YOU HAVE BEEN TAUGHT!

PART I
A MESSAGE

IN THE TIME OF HEROD KING OF JUDEA THERE WAS A PRIEST NAMED ZECHARIAH,
WHO BELONGED TO THE PRIESTLY DIVISION OF ABIJAH;
HIS WIFE ELIZABETH WAS ALSO A DESCENDANT OF AARON.
BOTH OF THEM WERE RIGHTEOUS IN THE SIGHT OF GOD, OBSERVING ALL THE LORD'S COMMANDS AND DECREES BLAMELESSLY...
BUT THEY WERE CHILDLESS.
BECAUSE ELIZABETH WAS NOT ABLE TO CONCEIVE, AND THEY WERE BOTH VERY OLD.

ONCE WHEN ZECHARIAH'S DIVISION WAS ON DUTY AND HE WAS SERVING AS PRIEST BEFORE GOD,
HE WAS CHOSEN BY LOT,
ACCORDING TO THE CUSTOM OF THE PRIESTHOOD,
TO GO INTO THE TEMPLE OF THE LORD
AND BURN INCENSE...

DO NOT BE AFRAID, ZECHARIAH!

YOUR PRAYER HAS BEEN HEARD!
YOUR WIFE ELIZABETH WILL BEAR YOU A SON,
AND YOU ARE TO CALL HIM JOHN.

HE WILL BE A JOY AND DELIGHT TO YOU, AND MANY WILL REJOICE BECAUSE OF HIS BIRTH,
FOR HE WILL BE GREAT IN THE SIGHT OF THE LORD.
HE IS NEVER TO TAKE WINE OR OTHER FERMENTED DRINK, AND HE WILL BE FILLED WITH THE HOLY SPIRIT EVEN BEFORE HE IS BORN.
HE WILL BRING BACK MANY OF THE PEOPLE OF ISRAEL TO THE LORD THEIR GOD.
AND HE WILL GO ON BEFORE THE LORD, IN THE SPIRIT AND POWER OF ELIJAH,
TO TURN THE HEARTS OF THE PARENTS TO THEIR CHILDREN AND THE DISOBEDIENT TO THE WISDOM OF THE RIGHTEOUS –
TO MAKE READY A PEOPLE PREPARED FOR THE LORD.

HOW CAN I BE SURE OF THIS? I AM AN OLD MAN AND MY WIFE IS WELL ON IN YEARS...
I AM GABRIEL!
I STAND IN THE PRESENCE OF GOD,
AND I HAVE BEEN SENT TO SPEAK TO YOU AND TO TELL YOU THIS GOOD NEWS!
AND NOW YOU WILL BE SILENT AND NOT ABLE TO SPEAK UNTIL THE DAY THIS HAPPENS,
BECAUSE YOU DID NOT BELIEVE MY WORDS, WHICH WILL COME TRUE AT THEIR APPOINTED TIME.

MEANWHILE,
THE PEOPLE WERE WAITING FOR ZECHARIAH AND WONDERING WHY HE STAYED SO LONG IN THE TEMPLE.
WHEN HE CAME OUT,
...
HE COULD NOT SPEAK TO THEM.
THEY REALISED HE HAD SEEN A VISION IN THE TEMPLE,
FOR HE KEPT MAKING SIGNS TO THEM BUT REMAINED UNABLE TO SPEAK.

AFTER THIS,
HIS WIFE ELIZABETH BECAME PREGNANT.
THE LORD HAS DONE THIS FOR ME.
IN THESE DAYS HE HAS SHOWN HIS FAVOUR...
AND TAKEN AWAY MY DISGRACE AMONG THE PEOPLE.

PART II
A PROMISE

IN THE SIXTH MONTH OF ELIZABETH'S PREGNANCY,
GOD SENT THE ANGEL GABRIEL TO NAZARETH, A TOWN IN GALILEE,

TO A VIRGIN...
PLEDGED TO BE MARRIED TO A MAN NAMED JOSEPH,
A DESCENDANT OF DAVID.
THE VIRGIN'S NAME WAS MARY...

GREETINGS, YOU WHO ARE HIGHLY FAVOURED!
THE LORD IS WITH YOU.
DO NOT BE AFRAID, MARY, YOU HAVE FOUND FAVOUR WITH GOD.
YOU WILL CONCEIVE AND GIVE BIRTH TO A SON,
AND YOU ARE TO CALL HIM...
JESUS.

HE WILL BE GREAT AND WILL BE CALLED THE SON OF THE MOST HIGH.
THE LORD GOD WILL GIVE HIM THE THRONE OF HIS FATHER DAVID, AND HE WILL REIGN OVER JACOB'S DESCENDANTS FOR EVER;
HIS KINGDOM WILL NEVER END...
HOW WILL THIS BE, SINCE I AM A VIRGIN?
THE HOLY SPIRIT WILL COME ON YOU, AND THE POWER OF THE MOST HIGH WILL OVERSHADOW YOU.
SO THE HOLY ONE TO BE BORN WILL BE CALLED THE SON OF GOD.
EVEN ELIZABETH YOUR RELATIVE IS GOING TO HAVE A CHILD IN HER OLD AGE,
AND SHE WHO WAS SAID TO BE UNABLE TO CONCEIVE IS IN HER SIXTH MONTH.
FOR NO WORD FROM GOD WILL EVER FAIL.
I AM THE LORD'S SERVANT, MAY YOUR WORD TO ME BE FULFILLED.

MARY GOT READY...
AND HURRIED TO A TOWN IN THE HILL COUNTRY OF JUDEA,

WHERE SHE ENTERED ZECHARIAH'S HOME AND GREETED ELIZABETH.
WHEN ELIZABETH HEARD MARY'S GREETING,
THE BABY LEAPED IN HER WOMB!
BLESSED ARE YOU AMONG WOMEN, AND BLESSED IS THE CHILD YOU WILL BEAR!
BUT WHY AM I SO FAVOURED, THAT THE MOTHER OF MY LORD SHOULD COME TO ME?
AS SOON AS THE SOUND OF YOUR GREETING REACHED MY EARS, THE BABY IN MY WOMB LEAPED FOR JOY.
BLESSED IS SHE WHO HAS BELIEVED THAT THE LORD WOULD FULFIL HIS PROMISES TO HER!

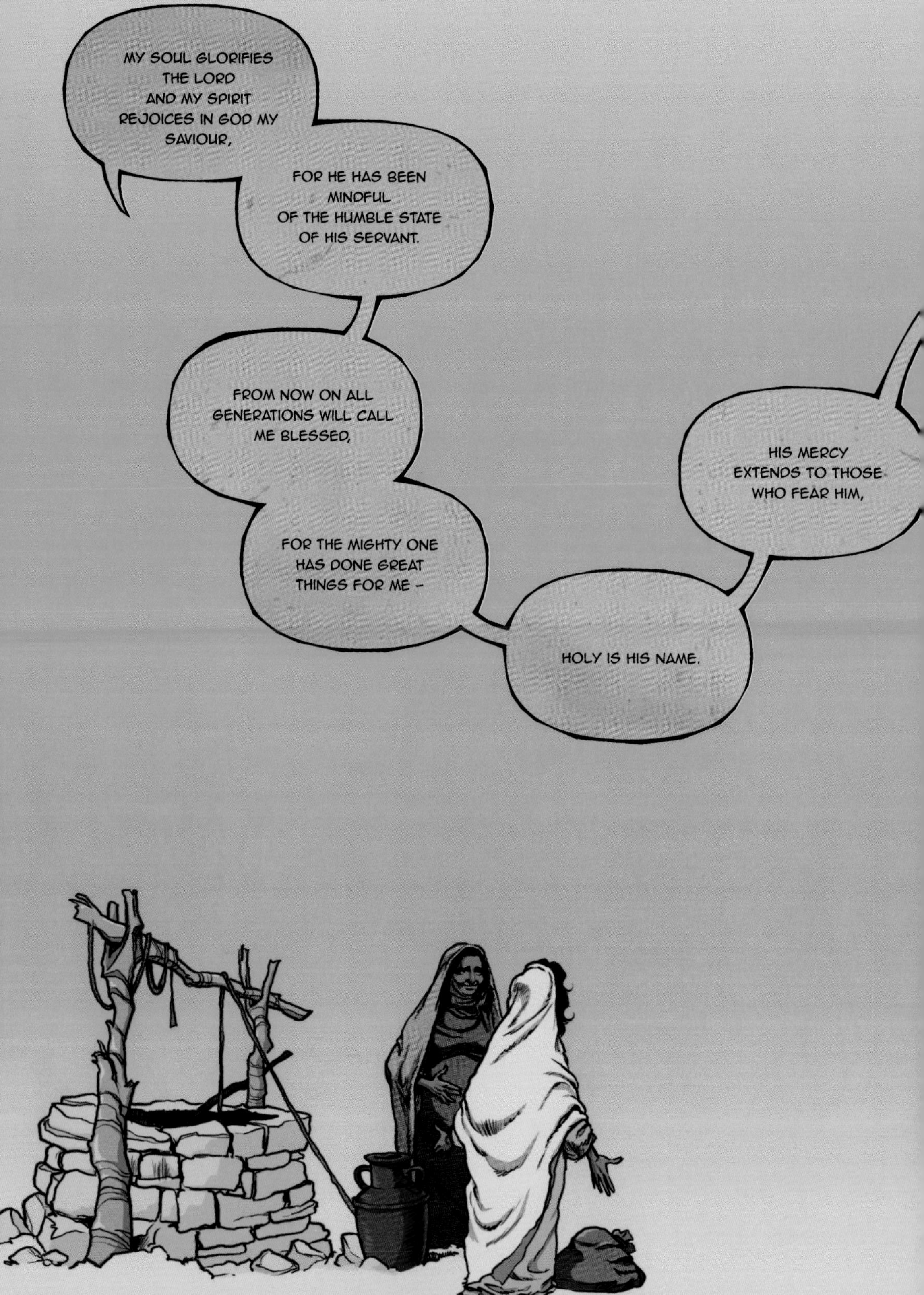
MY SOUL GLORIFIES THE LORD AND MY SPIRIT REJOICES IN GOD MY SAVIOUR,
FOR HE HAS BEEN MINDFUL OF THE HUMBLE STATE OF HIS SERVANT.
FROM NOW ON ALL GENERATIONS WILL CALL ME BLESSED,
FOR THE MIGHTY ONE HAS DONE GREAT THINGS FOR ME -
HOLY IS HIS NAME.
HIS MERCY EXTENDS TO THOSE WHO FEAR HIM,

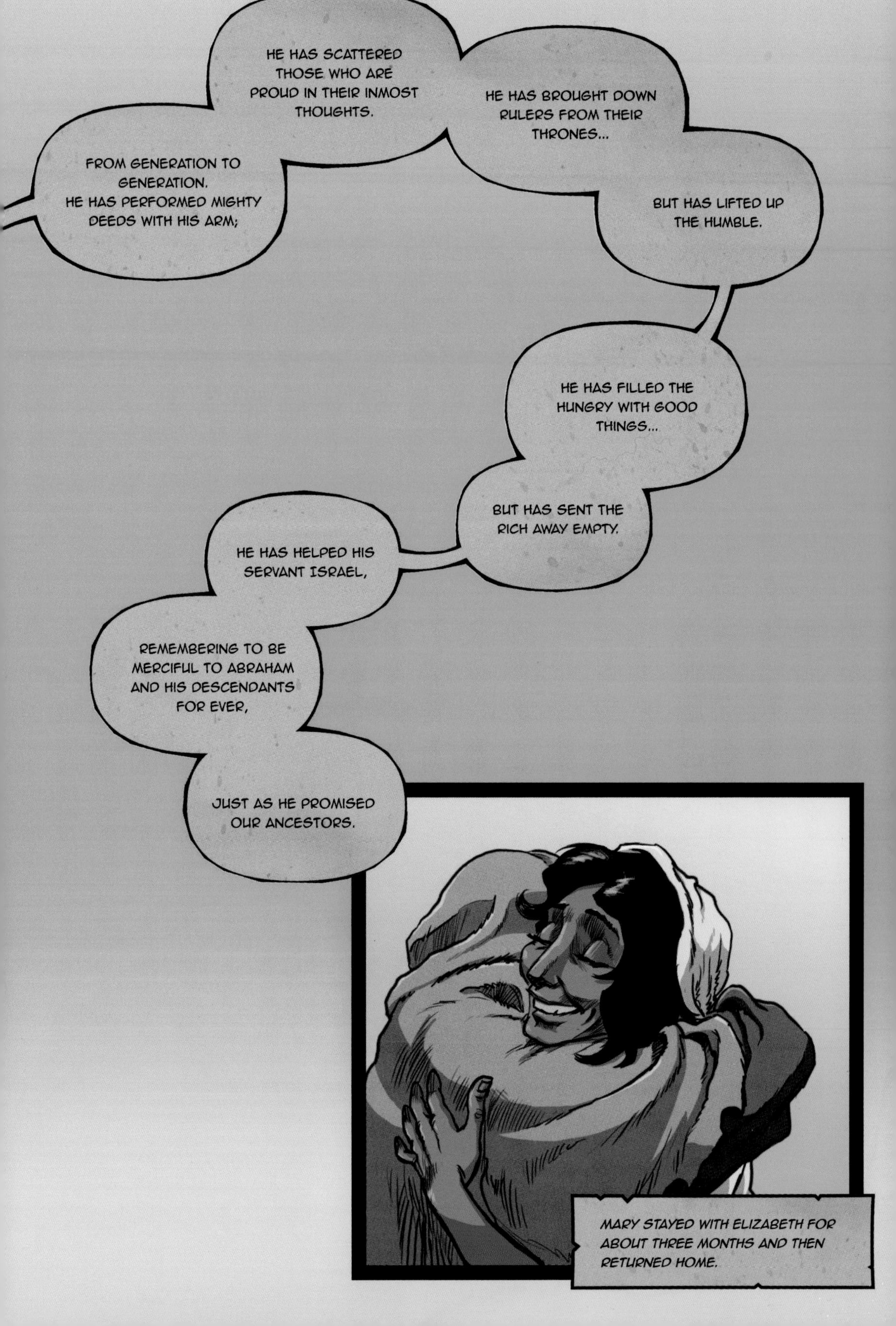
FROM GENERATION TO GENERATION. HE HAS PERFORMED MIGHTY DEEDS WITH HIS ARM;
HE HAS SCATTERED THOSE WHO ARE PROUD IN THEIR INMOST THOUGHTS.
HE HAS BROUGHT DOWN RULERS FROM THEIR THRONES...
BUT HAS LIFTED UP THE HUMBLE.
HE HAS FILLED THE HUNGRY WITH GOOD THINGS...
BUT HAS SENT THE RICH AWAY EMPTY.
HE HAS HELPED HIS SERVANT ISRAEL,
REMEMBERING TO BE MERCIFUL TO ABRAHAM AND HIS DESCENDANTS FOR EVER,
JUST AS HE PROMISED OUR ANCESTORS.
MARY STAYED WITH ELIZABETH FOR ABOUT THREE MONTHS AND THEN RETURNED HOME.

WHEN IT WAS TIME FOR ELIZABETH TO HAVE HER BABY,
SHE GAVE BIRTH TO A SON.
HER NEIGHBOURS AND RELATIVES HEARD THAT THE LORD HAD SHOWN HER GREAT MERCY, AND THEY SHARED HER JOY.
THEY WERE GOING TO NAME HIM AFTER HIS FATHER ZECHARIAH...

NO! HE IS TO BE CALLED JOHN.
THERE IS NO ONE AMONG YOUR RELATIVES WHO HAS THAT NAME.
'HIS NAME IS JOHN.'
WHAT THEN IS THIS CHILD GOING TO BE?
IMMEDIATELY ZECHARIAH'S MOUTH WAS OPENED AND HIS TONGUE SET FREE, AND HE BEGAN TO SPEAK, PRAISING GOD.

PRAISE BE TO THE LORD, THE GOD OF ISRAEL,
BECAUSE HE HAS COME TO HIS PEOPLE AND REDEEMED THEM.
HE HAS RAISED UP A HORN OF SALVATION FOR US
IN THE HOUSE OF HIS SERVANT DAVID
(AS HE SAID THROUGH HIS HOLY PROPHETS OF LONG AGO),
SALVATION FROM OUR ENEMIES
AND FROM THE HAND OF ALL WHO HATE US –
TO SHOW MERCY TO OUR ANCESTORS
AND TO REMEMBER HIS HOLY COVENANT,
THE OATH HE SWORE TO OUR FATHER ABRAHAM: TO RESCUE US FROM THE HAND OF OUR ENEMIES,
AND TO ENABLE US TO SERVE HIM WITHOUT FEAR
IN HOLINESS AND RIGHTEOUSNESS BEFORE HIM ALL OUR DAYS.

AND YOU, MY CHILD,
WILL BE CALLED A PROPHET OF THE MOST HIGH;
FOR YOU WILL GO ON BEFORE THE LORD TO PREPARE THE WAY FOR HIM,
TO GIVE HIS PEOPLE THE KNOWLEDGE OF SALVATION
THROUGH THE FORGIVENESS OF THEIR SINS,
BECAUSE OF THE TENDER MERCY OF OUR GOD,
BY WHICH THE RISING SUN WILL COME TO US FROM HEAVEN
TO SHINE ON THOSE LIVING IN DARKNESS AND IN THE SHADOW OF DEATH,
TO GUIDE OUR FEET INTO THE PATH OF PEACE.

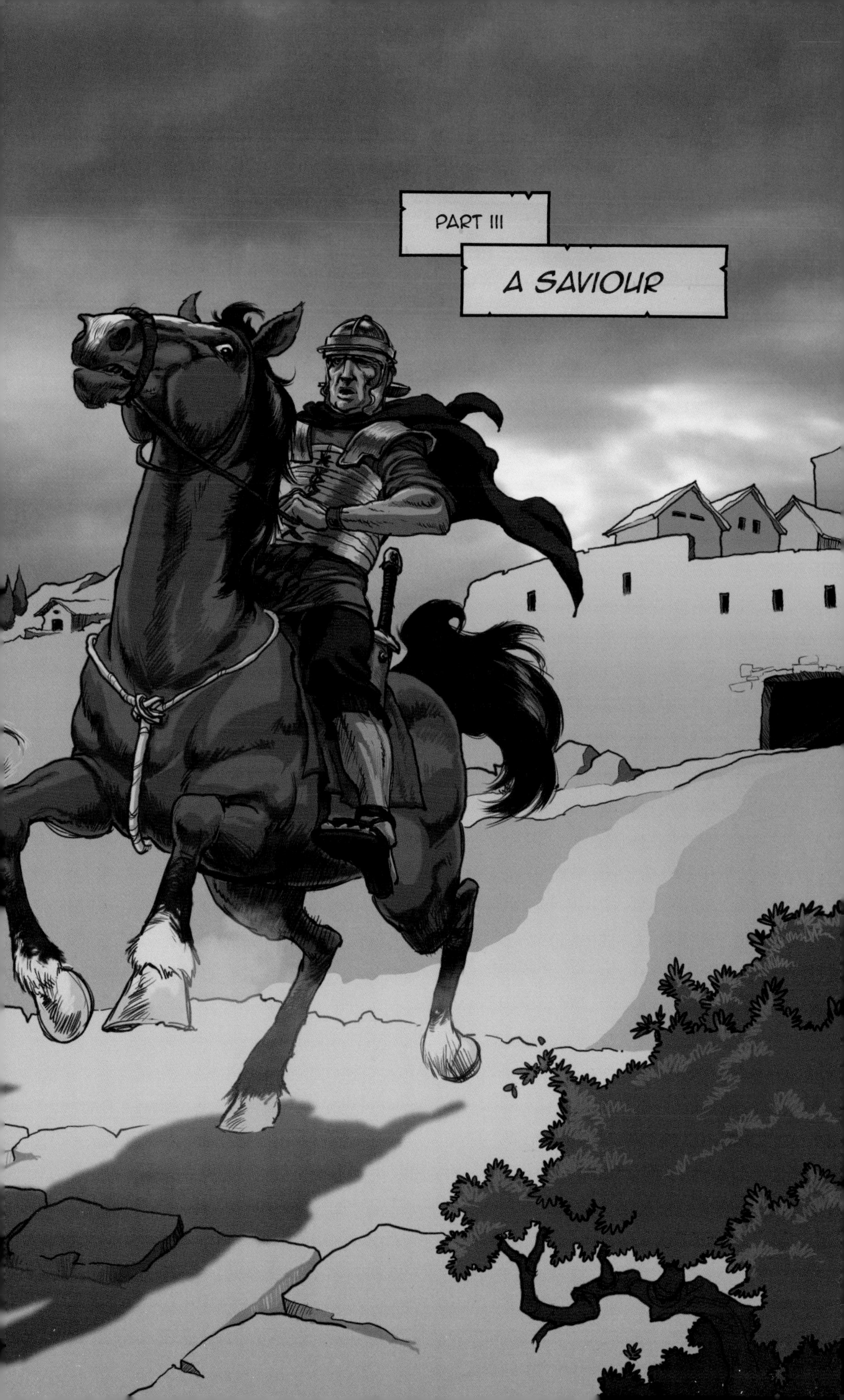
PART III
A SAVIOUR

IN THOSE DAYS CAESAR AUGUSTUS ISSUED A DECREE
THAT A CENSUS SHOULD BE TAKEN OF THE ENTIRE ROMAN WORLD.
AND EVERYONE WENT TO THEIR OWN TOWN TO REGISTER.

SO JOSEPH ALSO...
WENT UP FROM THE TOWN OF NAZARETH IN GALILEE TO JUDEA,
TO BETHLEHEM THE TOWN OF DAVID.
HE WENT THERE TO REGISTER WITH MARY, WHO WAS PLEDGED TO BE MARRIED TO HIM...
AND WAS EXPECTING A CHILD.

WHILE THEY WERE THERE,
THE TIME CAME FOR THE BABY TO BE BORN...
AND SHE GAVE BIRTH TO HER FIRSTBORN, A SON.
SHE WRAPPED HIM IN CLOTHS AND PLACED HIM IN A MANGER

THERE WERE SHEPHERDS LIVING OUT IN THE FIELDS NEAR BY,
KEEPING WATCH OVER THEIR FLOCKS AT NIGHT...

DO NOT BE AFRAID.

I BRING YOU GOOD NEWS THAT WILL CAUSE GREAT JOY FOR ALL THE PEOPLE.
TODAY IN THE TOWN OF DAVID A SAVIOUR HAS BEEN BORN
TO YOU!
HE IS THE MESSIAH,
THE LORD.
THIS WILL BE A SIGN TO YOU:
YOU WILL FIND A BABY WRAPPED IN CLOTHS,
AND LYING IN A MANGER.

GLORY TO GOD IN THE HIGHEST HEAVEN,
AND ON EARTH PEACE TO THOSE ON WHOM HIS FAVOUR RESTS.

LET'S GO TO BETHLEHEM AND SEE THIS THING THAT HAS HAPPENED,
WHICH THE LORD HAS TOLD US ABOUT.

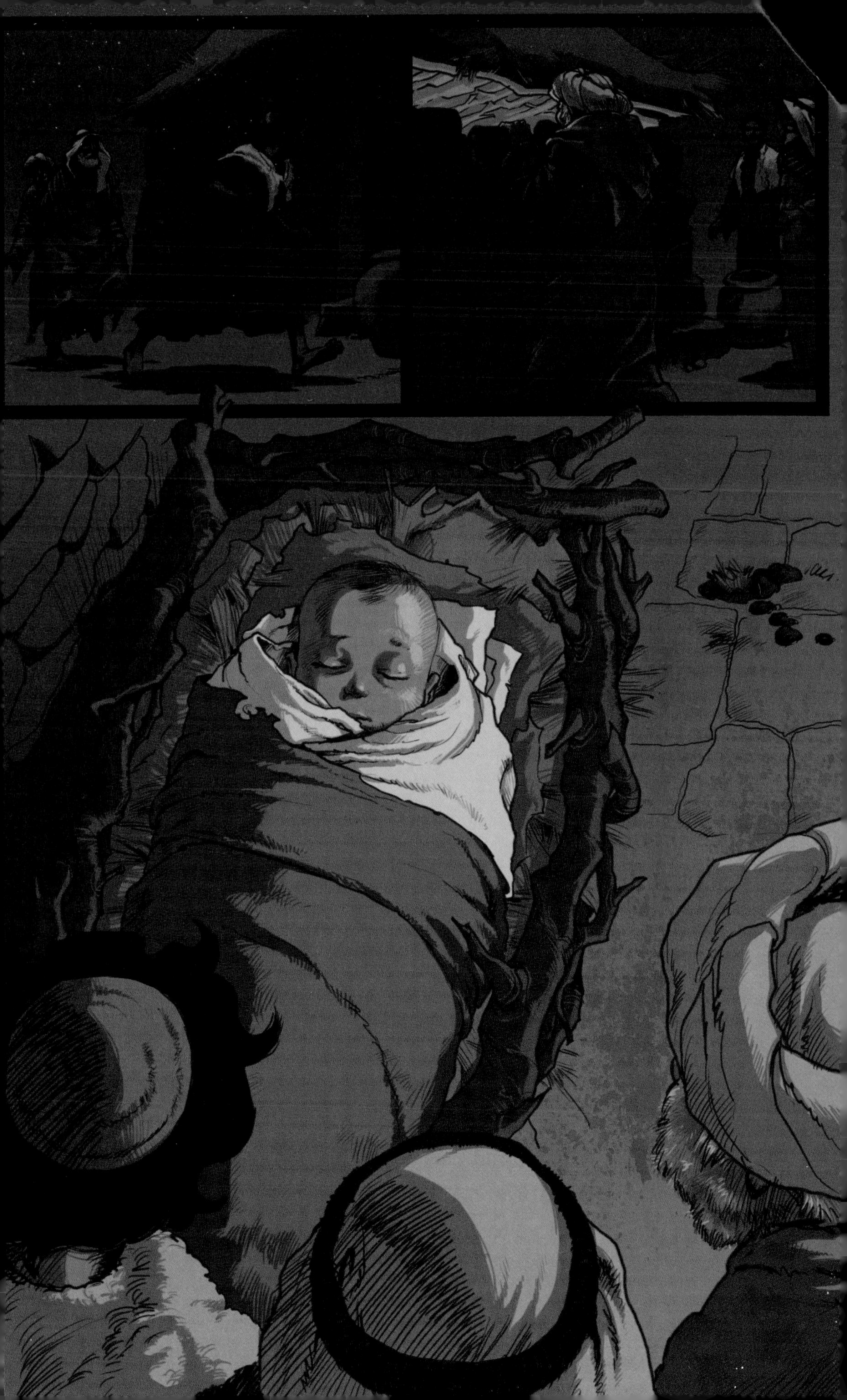

HEN THEY HAD SEEN HIM,
THEY SPREAD THE WORD CONCERNING WHAT HAD BEEN TOLD THEM ABOUT THIS CHILD,
AND ALL WHO HEARD IT WERE AMAZED AT WHAT THE SHEPHERDS SAID TO THEM.

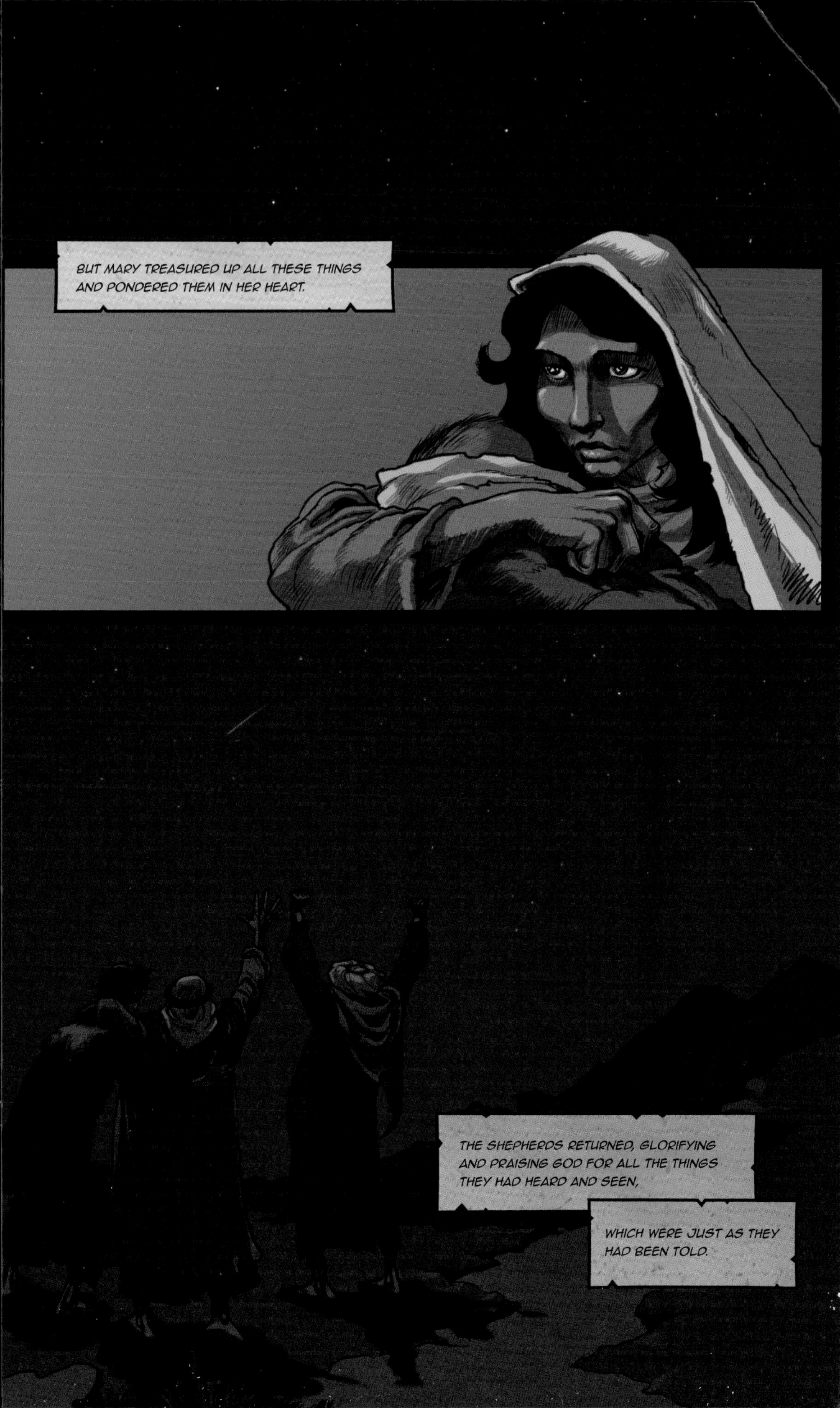
BUT MARY TREASURED UP ALL THESE THINGS AND PONDERED THEM IN HER HEART.
THE SHEPHERDS RETURNED, GLORIFYING AND PRAISING GOD FOR ALL THE THINGS THEY HAD HEARD AND SEEN,
WHICH WERE JUST AS THEY HAD BEEN TOLD.

HE EIGHTH DAY,
WHEN IT WAS TIME TO CIRCUMCISE THE CHILD,
HE WAS NAMED JESUS,
THE NAME THE ANGEL HAD GIVEN HIM BEFORE HE WAS CONCEIVED.
JOSEPH AND MARY TOOK HIM TO JERUSALEM TO PRESENT HIM TO THE LORD...
AND TO OFFER A SACRIFICE IN KEEPING WITH WHAT IS SAID IN THE LAW OF THE LORD:
'A PAIR OF DOVES OR TWO YOUNG PIGEONS'.

NOW THERE WAS A MAN IN JERUSALEM CALLED SIMEON,
WHO WAS RIGHTEOUS AND DEVOUT.
HE WAS WAITING FOR THE CONSOLATION OF ISRAEL,
AND THE HOLY SPIRIT WAS ON HIM.
IT HAD BEEN REVEALED TO HIM BY THE HOLY SPIRIT THAT HE WOULD NOT DIE BEFORE HE HAD SEEN THE LORD'S MESSIAH.
MOVED BY THE SPIRIT,
HE WENT INTO THE TEMPLE COURTS...

SOVEREIGN LORD, AS YOU HAVE PROMISED,
YOU MAY NOW DISMISS YOUR SERVANT IN PEACE!
FOR MY EYES HAVE SEEN YOUR SALVATION, WHICH YOU HAVE PREPARED IN THE SIGHT OF ALL NATIONS:
A LIGHT FOR REVELATION TO THE GENTILES, AND THE GLORY OF YOUR PEOPLE ISRAEL.
THIS CHILD IS DESTINED TO CAUSE THE FALLING AND RISING OF MANY IN ISRAEL,
AND TO BE A SIGN THAT WILL BE SPOKEN AGAINST, SO THAT THE THOUGHTS OF MANY HEARTS WILL BE REVEALED.
AND A SWORD WILL PIERCE YOUR OWN SOUL TOO.

THERE WAS ALSO A PROPHET, ANNA, THE DAUGHTER OF PENUEL, OF THE TRIBE OF ASHER.
SHE WAS VERY OLD; SHE HAD LIVED WITH HER HUSBAND SEVEN YEARS AFTER HER MARRIAGE,
AND THEN WAS A WIDOW UNTIL SHE WAS EIGHTY-FOUR.
SHE NEVER LEFT THE TEMPLE BUT WORSHIPPED NIGHT AND DAY, FASTING AND PRAYING.
COMING UP TO THEM AT THAT VERY MOMENT,
SHE GAVE THANKS TO GOD AND SPOKE ABOUT THE CHILD TO ALL WHO WERE LOOKING FORWARD TO THE REDEMPTION OF JERUSALEM.

WHEN JOSEPH AND MARY HAD DONE EVERYTHING REQUIRED BY THE LAW OF THE LORD,
THEY RETURNED TO GALILEE TO THEIR OWN TOWN OF NAZARETH.

AND THE CHILD GREW
AND BECAME STRONG;
HE WAS FILLED WITH WISDOM...

AND THE GRACE OF GOD WAS ON HIM.